POEMS TO SOLVE

POEMS TO SOLVE
BY MAY SWENSON

Charles Scribner's Sons   New York

J
811
S

POEMS TO SOLVE

CONTENTS

A CLUE OR TWO

Each of the poems in this selection, in one way or another, is a Poem to Solve.

A characteristic of all poetry, in fact, is that more is *hidden* in it than in prose.

A poem, read for the first time, can offer the same pleasure as opening a wrapped box. There is the anticipation of untying an intriguing knot of words, of unloosing all their intimations like loops, of lifting out—as if from under cover—an unexpected idea or fresh sensation.

Solving a poem can be like undoing a mysterious package. The identity or significance of what's inside may be concealed or camouflaged by the dimensions or shape of its "box." Sometimes, nested within a first discovery, another may be found — which in its turn contains still another — and so on. And if then you explore all the notions in the poem, you receive the added pleasure of seeing how they relate to each other in surprising ways, while at the same time combining to create the whole design of the "box."

Having opened or solved the poem and so enjoyed its contents, you can reassemble the parts again — re-imagine the whole into its original "closed" configuration. In this way you discover how the segments are shaped to interconnect.

The way that a poem is *unlike* a box is that it can enfold concepts within it that are larger than their container. Expansive elements in a poem can be packed magically into a tiny "space"—just as the word BIG, with only three letters, is *little*, yet conveys just the opposite meaning — or, conversely, the word INFINITESIMAL, which is *long*, thirteen letters, encompasses the notion of extremely small.

That is why we say of poetry that it has "magical properties"— and why we poets speak of our works as "paradoxical."

Notice how a poet's *games* are called his "works"— and how the "work" you do to solve a poem is really *play*. The impulse and motive for making a poem and for solving and enjoying a poem are quite alike: both include curiosity, alertness, joy in observation and invention.

Opening the box of a poem, looking under the wrappings and examining the various compartments can be absorbing and delightful. And, in addition to "what's in it for everybody," you may find an extra something hidden there especially for *you* — something that seems to mirror your secret feelings and thoughts, that strikes you as really true and worth keeping.

The "Riddle Poems" in the first section of this book all have in common the feature that the subject in each case is not named in either the title or the text. What each poem is about will gradually disclose itself. Poems in sections two and three employ organic metaphor, sound symbolism, verbal texture, and other devices. And all of them depend, as well, on elements of concealment of one sort or another, so as to leave intact for the young reader the pleasure of the unexpected, of discovery, and of solution.

These poems were selected with the aim of presenting the direct experience of finding and recognizing, comparing and contrasting, shaping and naming, solving and enjoying — thus inviting the reader to share with the poet some of the primary pleasures of the creative act itself.

—MAY SWENSON
April 1966

SOME RIDDLE POEMS

1 / AT BREAKFAST

Not quite
spherical
White
Oddly closed
and without a lid

A smooth miracle
here in my hand
Has it slid
from my sleeve?

The shape
of this box
keels me oval
Heels feel
its bottom
Nape knocks
its top

Seated
like a foetus
I look for
the dream-seam

What's inside?
A sun?

Off with its head
though it hasn't any
or is all head no body
a
One

Neatly
the knife scalps it
I scoop out
the braincap
soft
sweetly shuddering

Mooncream
this could be
Spoon
laps the larger
crescent
loosens a gilded
nucleus
from warm pap
A lyrical food

Opened
a seamless miracle
Ate a sun-germ
Good

2 / WAS WORM

Was worm

swaddled in white
Now tiny queen
in sequin coat
peacockbright

drinks the wind
and feeds
on sweat of the leaves

Is little chinks
of mosaic floating
a scatter
of colored beads

Alighting pokes
with her new black wire
the saffron yokes

On silent hinges
openfolds her wings'
applauding hands
Weaned

from coddling white
to lakedeep air
to blue and green

Is queen

3 / BY MORNING

Some for everyone
  plenty

  and more coming

Fresh   dainty   airily arriving
  everywhere at once

Transparent at first
  each faint slice
  slow   soundlessly tumbling

  then quickly thickly a gracious fleece
  will spread like youth   like wheat
  over the city

Each building will be   a hill
  all sharps made round

  dark worn noisy narrows made still
  wide   flat   clean   spaces

Streets will be   fields
  cars be   fumbling sheep

A deep bright harvest will be seeded
  in a night

By morning we'll be   children
  feeding on manna

  a new loaf on every doorsill

My body a rounded stone
with a pattern of smooth seams.
My head a short snake,
retractive, projective.
My legs come out of their sleeves
or shrink within,
and so does my chin.
My eyelids are quick clamps.

My back is my roof.
I am always at home.
I travel where my house walks.
It is a smooth stone.
It floats within the lake,
or rests in the dust.
My flesh lives tenderly
inside its bone.

5 / HYPNOTIST

His lair framed beneath the clock,
a red-haired beast hypnotic in the room
glazes our eyes and draws us close
with delicious snarls and flickers of his claws.
We stir our teacups and our wishes feast
on his cruelty.

Throw the Christian chairs to him,
a wild child in us cries.
Or let us be Daniel bared
to that seething maze his mane.
Loops of his fur graze the sill
where the clock's face looks scared.

Comfort-ensnared and languorous
our unused daring, roused, resembles him
fettered on the hearth's stage
behind the iron dogs.
He's the red locks of the sun
brought home to a cage.

Hunched before his flaring shape
we stir our teacups.
We wish he would escape
and loosen in ourselves the terrible.
But only his reflection pounces
on the parquet and the stair.

A green
string
is fastened
to the earth

at its apex
a yellow
circle

of silky
superimposed
spokes
The sun
is its mother

Later
the string
is taller
The circle
is white

an aureole
of evanescent
hairs
the wind
makes breathe

Later still
it is altered
the green
string
is thicker

the white
circle
bald
on one side

It is a half
circle
the wind lifts away

Roused from napping in my lap,
this nimble animal or five-legged star
parts its limbs sprat-wide.
See where they glide to focus at their base as spokes of a harp.
Blunt and fat the first,
sharp-tipped tapping the next,
the third authentic and the fourth shy,
the least, a runt, begs pardon for his stature. Why,
they're separate beasts I see, and not one beast with legs!

Or a family of dolls.
You could dress the tallest as a boy.
Already his sister wears a silver belt.
That's a toy-baby by her curled, if you put a bonnet on it.
Here's agile-joint, the pointed, the smart wife.
Square-head, short and papa-perfect, sits apart
in dignity, a wart at knuckle.

Turned over open, inner skin is vellum. Here's a map.
Five islands spread from the mainland in the fist.
Seen flat, it's a plain.
Forked rivers thread to the wrist,
or call them roads, the rosy pattern sprawled in an M.
Forests are stitched with prick-hatched pine-tree criss-marks.
Whorled lines are ploughed land. And
ending each pentacle beach are U-bands of sea-rippled sand.

Left one looked at, right one writes:
Star, Harp, Beast, Family of Five,
Map laid live in my lap.
Clapped together the two arrive, are stated,
the poem made, extremities mated.

0   A mouth. Can blow or breathe,
be funnel, or Hello.

1   A grass blade or a cut.

2   A question seated. And a proud
bird's neck.

3   Shallow mitten for two-fingered hand.

4   Three-cornered hut
on one stilt. Sometimes built
so the roof gapes.

5   A policeman. Polite.
Wearing visored cap.

6   O unrolling,
tape of ambiguous length
on which is written the mystery
of everything curly.

7   A step,
detached from its stair.

The universe in diagram:
A cosmic hourglass.
(Note enigmatic shape,
absence of any valve of origin,
how end overlaps beginning.)
Unknotted like a shoelace
and whipped back and forth,
can serve as a model of time.

 Lorgnette for the right eye.
In England or if you are Alice
the stem is on the left.

10 A grass blade or a cut
companioned by a mouth.
Open? Open. Shut? Shut.

/ SOUTHBOUND ON
THE FREEWAY

A tourist came in from Orbitville,
parked in the air, and said:

The creatures of this star
are made of metal and glass.

Through the transparent parts
you can see their guts.

Their feet are round and roll
on diagrams—or long

measuring tapes—dark
with white lines.

They have four eyes.
The two in the back are red.

Sometimes you can see a 5-eyed
one, with a red eye turning

on the top of his head.
He must be special—

the others respect him,
and go slow,

when he passes, winding
among them from behind.

They all hiss as they glide,
like inches, down the marked

tapes. Those soft shapes,
shadowy inside

the hard bodies—are they
their guts or their brains?

1   Awoke and stretched in all the bodies
    lofted on sinewy air. Clipped out
    beak-shaped cries and skinned the mist
    from the morning.

2   Stood wooden, wiggled in earth way under.
    A toenail scraped a mammoth's tusk.
    Jounced and jittered all these lippy leaves.

3   Slicked along meddling with rocks. Tore
    their ears off gradually. Sparkling made
    them hop and holler down a slate-cold throat.

4   Humped up, sucked in all my thongs
    belly-deep to the roaring core. Recoiled
    for a big yellow bloom. Burst and hurled
    wide open pods of light everywhere.

5   Loosened and looled elongate in hammocks
    of blue. Evasive of shape and the eggshell's
    curve. Without taint or tint or substance
    dissolved in fleecy sloth.

6   Pricked up out of each pore, urgent, ambitious,
    itching to be even. Scurried and spread
    so all is kept level. Forever unfinished
    my mass fernal mystery. Ants read its roots,
    tell its juices to sand.

7   Once cloud, now all memory my motion.
     Amorphous creeping slow as sleep to a full
     black gulping flood. The small five-fingered
     blot enlarged beyond identity. Heavy, unslaked,
     still hunting form. The hiding place,
     the necessary horror

     1 Birds   2 Tree   3 Waterfall   4 Sun
     5 Clouds   6 Grass   7 Shadow

The table of the pool is set.
Each cup quivers by a plate.

Some are filled with tea of sun,
some have pinks of liquor in;

some, thick and white, look upside down
as if put out to dry,

or not to use till morning
pours a thinner cream.

Lying out lopsided,
all the plates are green.

Immaculate as in Japan
the food is only dew,

but fountain-flounce, the table cloth,
shows a rainbow stain.

Some black-nosed goldfish passing through
on their way to shade

nudge the rocking saucers.
A wet ceramic toad,

descending stairs of moss
to breakfast on an insect,

upsets the level table top
but leaves the cups intact.

12 / THE SURFACE

First I saw the surface,
then I saw it flow,
then I saw the underneath.

In gradual light below
I saw a kind of room,
the ceiling was a veil,

a shape swam there
slow, opaque and pale.
I saw enter by a shifting corridor

other blunt bodies
that sank toward the floor.
I tried to follow deeper

with my avid eye.
Something changed the focus:
I saw the sky,

a glass between inverted trees.
Then I saw my face.
I looked until a cloud

flowed over that place.
Now I saw the surface
broad to its rim,

here gleaming, there opaque,
far out, flat and dim.
Then I saw it was an Eye:

I saw the Wink that slid
from underneath the rushes
before it closed its lid.

She does not place, relate or name
the objects of her hall,
nor bother to repair her ceiling,
sweep her floor or paint a wall
symmetrical with mountains;

cylindrical her tent
is pitched of ocean on one side
and—rakish accident—
forest on the other.
Granular, her rug

of many marbles, or of roots,
or needles, or a bog—
outrageous in its pattern;
the furniture is pine
and oak and birch and beech and elm;

the water couch is fine.
Mottled clouds and lightning rifts,
leaking stars and whole
gushing moons despoil her roof.
Contemptuous of control,

she lets a furnace burn all day,
she lets the winds be wild.
Broken, rotting, shambled things
lie where they like, are piled
on the same tables with her sweets,

her fruits and scented stuffs.
Her management is beauty.
Of careless silks and roughs,
rumpled rocks, the straightest rain,
blizzards, roses, crows,

April lambs and graveyards,
she *chances* to compose
a rich and sloven manor.
Her prosperous tapestries
are too effusive in design

for our analyses—
we who through her textures move,
we specks upon her glass,
who try to place, relate and name
all things within her mass.

5 CAT POEMS

4 BIRD POEMS

3 SEA POEMS

My cat jumps to the window sill
and sits there still as a jug.
He's waiting for me, but I cannot be
coming, for I am in the room.

His snout, a gloomy V of patience,
pokes out into the sun.
The funnels of his ears expect
to be poured full of my footsteps.

It, the electric moment, a sweet
mouse, will appear; at his gray
eye's edge I'll be coming home
if he sits on the window-ledge.

It is here, I say, and call him
to my lap. Not a hair
in the gap of his ear moves.
His clay gaze stays steady.

That solemn snout says: *It*
is what is about to happen, not
what is already here.

Cat takes a look at the weather.
Snow.
Puts a paw on the sill.
His perch is piled, is a pillow.

Shape of his pad appears.
Will it dig? No.
Not like sand.
Like his fur almost.

But licked, not liked.
Too cold.
Insects are flying, fainting down.
He'll try

to bat one against the pane.
They have no body and no buzz.
And now his feet are wet;
it's a puzzle.

Shakes each leg,
then shakes his skin
to get the white flies off.
Looks for his tail,

tells it to come on in
by the radiator.
World's turned queer
somehow. All white,

no smell. Well, here
inside it's still familiar.
He'll go to sleep until
it puts itself right.

Makes a platform for himself:
forepaws bent under his chest,
slot-eyes shut in a corniced head,
haunches high like a wing chair,
hindlegs parallel, a sled.

As if on water, low afloat
like a wooden duck: a bundle not
apt to be tipped, so symmetrized
on hidden keel of tail he rides
squat, arrested, glazed.

Lying flat, a violin:
hips are splayed, head and chin
sunk on paws, stem straight out
from the arched root
at the clef-curve of the thighs.

Wakes: the head ball rises.
Claws sprawl. Wires
go taut, make a wicket of his spine.
He humps erect, with scimitar yawn
of hooks and needles porcupine.

Sits, solid as a doorstop,
tail-encircled, tip laid on his toes,
ear-tabs stiff, gooseberry eyes
full, unblinking, sourly wise.
In outline: a demijohn with a pewter look.

Swivels, bends a muscled neck:
petal-of-tulip-tongue slicks
the brushpoint of his tail to black,
then smooths each glossy epaulette
with assiduous sponge.

Whistle him into a canter
into the kitchen: tail hooked aside,
ears at the ready. Elegant copy
of carrousel pony—
eyes bright as money.

17 / HIS SECRET

I took my cat apart
to see what made him purr.
Like an electric clock
or like the snore

of a warming kettle,
something fizzed and sizzled in him.
Was he a soft car,
the engine bubbling sound?

Was there a wire beneath his fur,
or humming throttle?
I undid his throat.
Within was no stir.

I opened up his chest
as though it were a door:
no whisk or rattle there.
I lifted off his skull:

no hiss or murmur.
I halved his little belly
but found no gear,
no cause for static.

So I replaced his lid,
laced his little gut.
His heart into his vest I slid
and buttoned up his throat.

His tail rose to a rod
and beckoned to the air.
Some voltage made him vibrate
warmer than before.

Whiskers and a tail:
perhaps they caught
some radar code
emitted as a pip, a dot-and-dash

of woolen sound.
My cat a kind of tuning-fork?—
amplifier?—telegraph?—
doing secret signal work?

His eyes elliptic tubes:
there's a message in his stare.
I stroke him
but cannot find the dial.

18 / FOREST

The pines, aggressive as erect tails of cats,
bob their tips when the wind freshens.

An alert breath like purring stirs below,
where I move timid over humps of hair,

crisp, shadow-brindled, heaving as if
exhilarated muscular backs felt

the wisps of my walking. Looking to sky,
glaring then closing between the slow

lashes of boughs, I feel observed:
up high are oblong eyes that know,

as their slits of green light
expand, squeeze shut, expand,

that I stand here. Suddenly I go,
flick-eyed, hurrying over fur

needles that whisper as if they weren't dead.
My neck-hairs rise. The feline forest grins

behind me. Is it about to follow?
Which way out through all these whiskered yawns?

A bird
is perched
upon a wing
The wing
is stone
The bird
is real
A drapery
falls about this form
The form is stone
The dress is rain
The pigeon preens his own
and does not know
he sits upon a wing.
The angel does not feel
a relative among her large
feathers stretch
and take his span
in charge
and leave her there
with her cold
wings that cannot fold
while his fan
in air
The fountain raining
wets the stone,
but does not know it dresses
an angel in its tresses
Her stone cheek smiles
and does not care
that real tears
flow there

20 / FEEL LIKE A BIRD

Feel like a   Bird
Understand
He has no   Hand

Instead a   Wing
Close-lapped
mysterious thing

In sleeveless coat
he halves the   Air
skipping there

like water-licked boat
Lands on   Star-Toes
Finger-beak in

feather-pocket
finds no   Coin
In neat head like   Seeds

in a quartered apple
eyes join
sniping at   Opposites

to stereoscope
the scene before
Close to floor   Giddy

no arms to fling
a third   Sail
spreads for calm

his tail
Hand better than a   Wing
to gather a   Heap

to count
to clasp a   Mate?
Or leap

lone-free on muffled
shoulders to span
a   Fate?

As if the knob
perhaps of porcelain
of a small calliope
were turned around twice

then a hush
while the memory
of the dainty fragment
is listened to by the box itself

the hermit thrush
that plain instrument
not seeming precious
twice releases its throb

This double jewel
this melodious jangle
is all there's in it
One expects the knob to spin

and in a rush
a long-looped ornament of every color
to dangle down the air
A spoke in there

is not broken
That stunted quirk
repeated
with attention to the silence in between

is the amulet
that makes the charm box work
The hermit thrush
refuses to be luscious

to elaborate to entangle
to interpret
or even to declare a goal
Only the strict reiteration of a rarity

from this small calliope
until it is convinced its bare
beginning is the end
and the whole

The binocular owl,
fastened to a limb
like a lantern
all night long,

sees where all
the other birds sleep:
towhee under leaves,
titmouse deep

in a twighouse,
sapsucker gripped
to a knothole lip,
redwing in the reeds,

swallow in the willow,
flicker in the oak—
but cannot see poor
whip-poor-will

under the hill
in deadbrush nest,
who's awake, too—
with stricken eye

flayed by the moon—
her brindled breast
repeats, repeats, repeats its plea
for cruelty.

The sea comes up and the sun goes over
    The sea goes out and the sun falls
The stubby shadow of the lighthouse pales
    stretches to a finger and inches east
The wind lifts from off the sea
    and curries and curries the manes of the dunes
The pipers and the terns skate over
    tweaking the air with their talk
In sky clean as a cat-licked dish
    clouds are sandbars bared by ebbing blue

The hourglass is reversed

The sea comes up and the moon peers over
    The sea goes out and the moon swells
The shadow of the lighthouse thick as a boot
    is swiped by a whiskered beam
The wind licks at the jetty stones
    The pipers and terns hunch on the spit
hiding their necks and stilted feet
    The sky has caught a netful of stars
The moon is a dory trolling them in

The hourglass is reversed

The sea comes up and the moon tips under
    The sea goes out and the sun looms
The sun is a schooner making for harbor
    Shallops of cloud are adrift in the west
The wind gallops the waves to a lather
    and lashes the grass that shines on the dunes
The lighthouse looks at its twin in the water
    The pipers and terns preen on its brow

The wave-shaped dune is still.
Its curve does not break,
though it looks as if it will,

like the head of the dune-
shaped wave advancing,
its ridge strewn

with white shards flaking.
A sand-faced image of the wave
is always in the making.

Opposite the sea's rough glass
cove, the sand's smooth-whittled cave
under the brow of grass

is sunny and still. Rushing
to place its replica
on the shore, the sea is pushing

sketches of itself
incessantly into the foreground.
All the models smash upon the shelf,

but grain by grain the creeping sand
reërects their profiles
and makes them stand.

Thick twisted cables
            of bottle glass at the base,
gunbarrel-blue higher up,
  are quickly being braided and stretched
their condition molten,
                        their surface cold.
Or they are the long smooth logs of a pile
            being built from the top down.
The trunks of greatest girth
                arrive at the bottom
with silver rips and ridges in their bark.

            There is a wall in motion
like a lathe of light
                and dark galvanic blue
layers which are twirling,
    extending beyond your eye-points.
You cannot see their ends.

        Watch the topmost thinnest strand,
too taut to quiver:
            Above is a calcimined ceiling,
heliotrope . . . steady . . .
                delicate as for a bedroom.

SOME OTHER POEMS
TO FIND AND SOLVE

26 / GREEN RED BROWN
AND WHITE

Bit an apple on its red
side. Smelled like snow.
Between white halves broken open,
brown winks slept in sockets of green.

Stroked a birch white as a thigh,
scar-flecked, smooth as the neck
of a horse. On mossy pallets green
the pines dropped down
their perfect carvings brown.

Lost in the hairy wood,
followed berries red
to the fork. Had to choose
between green and green. High

in a sunwhite dome a brown bird
sneezed. Took the path least likely
and it led me home. For

each path leads both out and in.
I come while going. No to and from.
There is only here. And here
is as well as there. Wherever
I am led I move within the care
of the season,
hidden in the creases of her skirts
of green or brown or beaded red.

And when they are white,
I am not lost. I am not lost then,
only covered for the night.

Long, glossy caterpillar
with softest feet
of audible and inaudible vowels;

dewberry head so black
it's silver;
nippered lip, and fluent rump;

who moves by the T
at his tifted middle,
a little locomotive hump.

His ripple is felt
by the palm ashamed,
and we are loath to name him;

hairs of his back
a halo's paint
we daren't put round objects any more.

He's tainted,
doomed to sloth, like those
other lunar insects such

as Velvet
that we must not touch,
or Rose, or Gold.

His destiny—
a myth or moth—still glows
inside the skull,

although his creep is blue,
the untrusted phosphor
of our sleep.

In the pond in the park
all things are doubled:
Long buildings hang and
wriggle gently. Chimneys
are bent legs bouncing
on clouds below. A flag
wags like a fishhook
down there in the sky.

The arched stone bridge
is an eye, with underlid
in the water. In its lens
dip crinkled heads with hats
that don't fall off. Dogs go by,
barking on their backs.
A baby, taken to feed the
ducks, dangles upside-down,
a pink balloon for a buoy.

Treetops deploy a haze of
cherry bloom for roots,
where birds coast belly-up
in the glass bowl of a hill;
from its bottom a bunch
of peanut-munching children
is suspended by their
sneakers, waveringly.

A swan, with twin necks
forming the figure three,
steers between two dimpled
towers doubled. Fondly
hissing, she kisses herself,
and all the scene is troubled:
water-windows splinter,
tree-limbs tangle, the bridge
folds like a fan.

Above my face is a map
where continents form and fade.
Blue countries, made
on a white sea, are erased;
white countries are traced
on a blue sea.

It is a map that moves
faster than real
but so slow;
only my watching proves
that island has being,
or that bay.

It is a model of time;
mountains are wearing away,
coasts cracking, the ocean
spills over, then new
hills heap into view
with river-cuts of blue between them.

It is a map of change:
this is the way things are
with a stone or a star.
This is the way things go,
hard or soft,
swift or slow.

Body my house
my horse my hound
what will I do
when you are fallen

Where will I sleep
How will I ride
What will I hunt

Where can I go
without my mount
all eager and quick
How will I know
in thicket ahead
is danger or treasure
when Body my good
bright dog is dead

How will it be
to lie in the sky
without roof or door
and wind for an eye

With cloud for shift
how will I hide

Watch and watch and follow me
I am all green mimicry
          In my manyness you see
what engenders my beauty

     Dancer red and gold with greed
I am that which does not bleed
     On my rising breath be carried
Twine with me and so be freed

     Ride with me and hold my mane
I am chimaera the skein
          of everchange that's lily-lain
above the steady mountain

               Go the circle of my cage
I own nothing but my rage
     the black and white of the savage
This singleness may you assuage

1   At moment X
    the universe began.
    It began at point X.
    Since then,
    through The Hole in a Nozzle,
    stars have spewed. An
    inexhaustible gush
    populates the void forever.

2   The universe was there
    before time ran.
    A grain
    slipped in the glass:
    the past began.
    The Container
    of the Stars expands;
    the sand
    of matter multiplies forever.

3   From zero radius
    to a certain span,
    the universe, A Large Lung
    specked with stars,
    inhales time
    until, turgent, it can
    hold no more,
    and collapses. Then
    space breathes, and inhales again,
    and breathes again: Forever.

the stone
would like to be
Alive like me

the rooted tree
longs to be Free

the mute beast
envies my fate
Articulate

on this Ball
half dark half light
i walk Upright
i lie Prone
within the night

beautiful each Shape
to see
wonderful each Thing
to name
here a stone
there a tree
here a River
there a Flame

marvelous to Stroke
the patient beasts
within their yoke

how i Yearn
for the lion
in his den
though he spurn
the touch of men

the longing
that I know
is in the Stone also
it must be
the same that rises
in the Tree
the longing
in the Lion's call
speaks for all

oh to Endure
like the stone
sufficient to itself alone

or Reincarnate
like the tree
be born each spring
to greenery

or like the lion
without law
to roam the Wild
on velvet paw

but if walking i meet
a Creature like me
on the street
two-legged
with human face
to recognize is to Embrace

wonders pale
beauties dim

during my delight
with Him

an Evolution strange
two Tongues touch
exchange
a Feast unknown
to stone
or tree or beast

34 / A BOY LOOKING AT BIG DAVID

I'm touching his toe.
I know I'll be brave after this.
His toenail wide as my hand,
I have to stand tall to reach it.

The big loose hand with the rock in it
by his thigh
is high above my head. The vein
from wrist to thumb, a blue strain in the marble.

As if it had natural anatomy all its own
inside it.
Somebody skinned off the top stone,
and there He stands.

I'd like to climb up there on that slippery Hip,
shinny up to the Shoulder
the other side of that thumping Neck,
and lie in the ledge on the collar-bone,

by the sling.
In that cool place
I'd stare-worship that big, full-lipped,
frown-browed, far-eyed, I-dare-you-Face.

I'd like to live on that David for a while,
get to know
how to be immortal like Him.
But I can only reach his Toe—

broad, poking over the edge of the stand.
So cool . . .
Maybe, marble Him,
he likes the warm of my hand?

35 / THE CENTAUR

The summer that I was ten—
Can it be there was only one
summer that I was ten? It must

have been a long one then—
each day I'd go out to choose
a fresh horse from my stable

which was a willow grove
down by the old canal.
I'd go on my two bare feet.

But when, with my brother's jack-knife,
I had cut me a long limber horse
with a good thick knob for a head,

and peeled him slick and clean
except a few leaves for the tail,
and cinched my brother's belt

around his head for a rein,
I'd straddle and canter him fast
up the grass bank to the path,

trot along in the lovely dust
that talcumed over his hoofs,
hiding my toes, and turning

his feet to swift half-moons.
The willow knob with the strap
jouncing between my thighs

was the pommel and yet the poll
of my nickering pony's head.
my head and my neck were mine,

yet they were shaped like a horse.
My hair flopped to the side
like the mane of a horse in the wind.

My forelock swung in my eyes,
my neck arched and I snorted.
I shied and skittered and reared,

stopped and raised my knees,
pawed at the ground and quivered.
My teeth bared as we wheeled

and swished through the dust again.
I was the horse and the rider,
and the leather I slapped to his rump

spanked my own behind.
Doubled, my two hoofs beat
a gallop along the bank,

the wind twanged in my mane,
my mouth squared to the bit.
And yet I sat on my steed

quiet, negligent riding,
my toes standing the stirrups,
my thighs hugging his ribs.

At a walk we drew up to the porch.
I tethered him to a paling.
Dismounting, I smoothed my skirt

and entered the dusky hall.
My feet on the clean linoleum
left ghostly toes in the hall.

Where have you been? said my mother.
Been riding, I said from the sink,
and filled me a glass of water.

What's that in your pocket? she said.
Just my knife. It weighted my pocket
and stretched my dress awry.

Go tie back your hair, said my mother,
and *Why is your mouth all green?*
*Rob Roy, he pulled some clover
as we crossed the field,* I told her.